FINDING OUT ABOUT BIRDS

By
William C. Dilger, Ph. D.
Assistant Director of Research
Laboratory of Ornithology
Cornell University

Illustrated by the Author

FINDING-OUT BOOKS

HOME LIBRARY PRESS
New York, N. Y.

©
Copyright 1963

WILLIAM C. DILGER

Library of Congress Catalog No. 63—13694

ACKNOWLEDGEMENTS

Photographs for the eight-page color insert, VARIATION IN BIRDS and endpapers were supplied by **Arthur A. Allen,** Cornell University. Photographs for the Cover are by **Russ Kinne** of Photo Researchers, Inc.

Insert Design by **Morton Garchik**

Manufactured in the United States of America

CONTENTS U. S.1224704

See page 9

ICHTHYORNIS

Introduction

BIRDS ARE vertebrate (backboned) animals along with fish, amphibians, reptiles, and mammals. Birds and mammals, unlike all the other vertebrate animals, are warm-blooded. This means that their body temperatures are relatively independent of the surrounding air temperature. Despite rather great differences in form and color, all birds are easily recognized because of their *feathers*. No other group of animals possess these. Of course, there are other distinctly avian features and some of these are discussed later.

It is certain that birds gradually evolved from reptiles. Unfortunately, however, the fossil evidence is rather sparse. Consequently, many details are still lacking but the main outline of their evolutionary history is clear.

The earliest known bird is *Archaeopteryx* (ancient wing). Several fossils of this species have been found in the lithographic limestone deposits of Bavaria. This limestone was deposited during the Jurassic period of time so that we know that *Archaeopteryx* lived about one hundred and thirty million years ago. It had many bird-like features such as feathers, wings, and bird-like hind legs. However, many reptilian features were still present. Among these are teeth, unfused pelvic bones, and the presence of many bones in the tail.

The fossil record is blank for about the next thirty to thirty-five million years. Then, from certain beds of shale laid down during the Cretaceous period of time, many fossils were found. About twenty different kinds of birds have been identified so far. These include eight different kinds resembling *Hesperornis* (a rather large, flightless, and toothed diving bird), about the same number of kinds similar to *Ichthyornis* (strong-flying and probably toothless birds resembling modern gulls), flamingos, a cormorant, a goose-like bird called *Gallornis,* and an ostrich-like bird named *Caenognathus.* The *Hesperornis* and *Ichthyornis* type birds died out and apparently left no descendants. This occurred when the great inland seas of the Cretaceous period finally dried up.

The next glimpse we have is of birds which lived about sixty million years ago in the Eocene epoch of time. Many of these resembled modern birds such as herons, ducks, grouse, sandpipers, cranes, rails, and owls. Others were quite unlike modern birds and apparently did not lead to any of our modern groups. Among these was *Diatryma,* a heavily built flightless giant standing over six feet high.

Fossil birds become progressively more numerous in the increasingly younger geologic deposits and more modern species become more frequent. In North America, the richest deposits of bird fossils are found in deposits characteristic of the Pleistocene epoch of time which began about one million years ago. At this time, many present day species were already in existence (all present major groups of birds were probably in existence as long ago as the Miocene epoch, about twenty million years ago, and some even earlier).

7

PASSERIFORMES
SONGBIRDS LXIX, 5650

TROGONIIFORMES
TROGONS I, 34

PICIFORMES
WOODPECKERS VI, 395

CORACIIFORMES KINGFISHERS, ROLLERS, ETC, X, 195

COLIIFORMES
COLIES I, 6

APODIFORMES
SWIFTS, HUMMINGBIRDS III, 404

STRIGIFORMES
OWLS II, 143

CAPRIMULGIFORMES
WHIP-POOR-WILLS, ETC. V, 95

CUCULIFORMES
CUCKOOS II, 149

PSITTACIFORMES
PARROTS I, 326

COLUMBIFORMES
DOVES, ETC. II, 318

CHARADRIIFORMES
PLOVERS, ETC. XVI, 213

GRUIFORMES
CRANES, RAILS, ETC. XII, 196

GALLIFORMES
PHEASANTS, ETC. VII, 275

FALCONIFORMES
HAWKS, EAGLES, FALCONS V, 208

ANSERIFORMES
DUCKS, GEESE, ETC. II, 170

CICONIIFORMES
STORKS, HERONS, ETC. VII, 124

PELECANIFORMES
PELICANS, GANNETS, ETC. VI, 58

PROCELLARIIFORMES
PETRELS, SHEARWATERS, ALBATROSSES, IV, 105

COLYMBIFORMES
GREBES I, 18

GAVIIFORMES
LOONS I, 4

TINAMIFORMES
TINAMOUS I, 51

APTERYGIFORMES
KIWIS I, 3

CASUARIIFORMES
CASSOWARIES II, 7

RHEIFORMES
RHEAS I, 2

SPHENISCIFORMES
PENGUINS I, 17

STRUTHIONIFORMES
OSTRICH I, 1

BIRDS — FAMILIES AND SPECIES

8   ROMAN NUMERALS = Number of Families   ARABIC NUMERALS = Number of Species

RELATIONSHIPS AND DISTRIBUTION OF MODERN BIRDS

ALL BIRDS, both past and present, are placed in the *class Aves.* Each of the other major groups of vertebrate animals is also a class (fish: Pisces, amphibians: Amphibia, reptiles: Reptilia, and mammals: Mammalia). The class Aves is further divided into two subclasses called *Archaeornithes* (ancient birds) and *Neornithes* (modern birds). Archaeornithes contains only the now extinct *Archaeopteryx.* All other birds, even those of Cretaceous times, are placed in Neornithes. This subclass is further divided into groupings called *orders.* Many entire orders are now extinct. Examples of extinct orders are Hesperornithiformes to which *Hesperornis* belongs and Ichthyornithiformes to which *Ichthyornis* belongs (all order names end in "formes"). There are about twenty-seven living orders of birds. An exact number cannot be given because authorities differ on just what constitutes an order. On the opposite page is a diagram showing the orders of birds and their relationships to one another.

The orders are further divided into *families.* Family names always end in "idae." All of the families belonging to the same order are more closely related to one another than they are to families contained in other orders. There are about one hundred and sixty families of birds in the world. Families are divided into *genera* (singular: genus). There may be several species in each genus. The

ARCHAEOPTERYX

HESPERORNIS

singular of species is still species—*not* specie! An example of two birds in the same genus is the American Robin, *Turdus migratorius,* and the European Blackbird, *Turdus merula.* There are also other species in the genus *Turdus.* The name of a genus or of a full species is always either underlined or italicized for emphasis. All other scientific names are capitalized (like a genus name) but not underlined or italicized. Following is a sample classification of the American Robin and the European Blackbird:

> Class: Aves (birds)
> Subclass: Neornithes (modern birds)
> Order: Passeriformes (perching birds)
> Family: Turdidae (thrushes)
> Genus: *Turdus* (typical thrushes)
> Species: *Turdus migratorius* (American Robin)

Turdus merula (European Blackbird)

The full species name may be followed by a third name which designates the *subspecies.* A subspecies is a population within a species which differs slightly but consistently from other similar populations within a species. For example: *Turdus migratorius migratorius* (Eastern Robin) and *Turdus migratorius achrusterus* (Southern Robin). Other categories have been used in an effort to express the relationships of birds even more exactly. Some of these are suborders, subfamilies, subgenera, superfamilies, tribes, and so forth.

Birds are found throughout the entire world from the arctic to the antarctic and inhabit a great variety of habitats. Some are very widely distributed and are able to live in many areas. The familiar Barn Owl is a good example. There are many species, however, that are more restricted in their ranges and some are confined to very small areas indeed. Some may only occur on one mountain or on one small island.

Natural Selection

Through the process of *natural selection*, birds have evolved a variety of adaptive responses to features present in different environments. Natural selection works by having the probability of survival of each individual slightly different from the probability of survival of other individuals. This is made possible because, except for identical twins, no two individuals are *exactly* alike. This is one of the reasons you can tell your friends apart. Those individuals which happen to be better adapted to survive, have the greatest probability that they will survive and, of course, these will then pass their traits along to their descendants. Over long periods of time, the characteristic features of entire populations gradually change. We now know that all of the birds we see around us are the products of at least one hundred and thirty million years of such gradual change. You may recall that our earliest known bird fossil is about one hundred and thirty million years old. This change is still going on and one hundred and thirty million years from now will see further great changes in birds.

DIATRYMA

The Pressure of Environment

One would think that once a population became perfectly adapted to any particular environment it would not change any more. The reasons these changes go on anyway is because the environments keep changing. They become warmer or colder, sunnier or cloudier, wetter or drier, and so on. Sometimes animals can not evolve fast enough to become adapted well enough to survive. They then may become extinct if they can not gradually shift their ranges to more suitable conditions.

Some of the important features of environments which exert selective pressures on survival and, hence, influence the course of evolution are the kinds and availability of food; the nature and amount of vegetation; the kinds of predators present; the presence or absence of closely related kinds which provide competition for food, mates, nesting sites, and so forth; and features of climate such as rainfall, winds, temperatures, humidity, and the nature of the seasons.

Much can be told about the diet and habitat of a bird merely by looking at it. If one looks at the long legs and neck of an ostrich it is obvious that it is capable of running at high speeds over flat, open country and is able to see great distances. Its rather unspecialized bill makes us suspect that its diet is equally unspecialized and that it can eat a great variety of foods. The compact, streamlined falcon equipped with sharply hooked bill, strong wings, rather long tail, and needle sharp talons tells us that this bird is a meat-eater which is capable of pursuing and catching very fast and agile prey. The long legs and neck coupled with a dagger-like bill tells us that a heron feeds by wading in water and grasping fish and other aquatic animals. The strong wings and tiny feet characteristic of swifts and hummingbirds tells us that they spend most of their waking hours in the air. You will learn other ways of predicting various features of a bird's way of life as you read the remaining sections of this book. Be careful to always check your predictions by watching the actual bird because mistakes can be made!

Birds, along with all other living things, have the problem of staying alive long enough to adequately reproduce their own kind; otherwise they would become extinct. This basic problem is frequently broken down into two problems: 1) staying alive and healthy as an individual and 2) reproducing. The following sections on the structures and behaviors of birds will tell you some of the ways this is done.

AMERICAN ROBIN

EUROPEAN BLACKBIRD

THE STRUCTURE OF BIRDS

BIRDS, IN general, present a streamlined shape which is adapted to their free passage through air during flight. This streamlining is partly due to their covering of feathers which fill in any unstreamlined features of their anatomy. Feathers also make excellent waterproofing and also contain myriads of tiny air spaces among them which serve as insulation against heat and cold. In addition, the feathers may be adjusted to create the best insulating conditions for varying external temperatures. The feathers may be pressed tightly to the body thus destroying most of the trapped air spaces if the bird is too warm. Such a feather adjustment is termed *sleeked*. The feathers may be erected a little all over the body thus increasing the amount of trapped air. This condition is called *fluffed*. A bird which is too cold will do this.

Birds which are ill become fluffed because they are typically cold also. A bird may erect its feathers even more and present a rather ragged appearance. This feather posture is called *ruffled*. Birds do this if they are very hot. The feathers do not touch at their tips thus allowing cooling air to circulate over the skin. Normally, feathers are held in a position between that of sleeked and fluffed. This is termed *relaxed* plumage.

Plumage

The entire feather covering of a bird is termed *plumage* and may be colored and patterned in different ways which increase their owner's probability of survival. The plumage may blend in with the bird's environment. This type of coloration and pattern is called *cryptic*. Cryptic plumages are generally various shades of grey or brown, and sometimes green or

PENGUIN

TOUCAN

PETREL

CACTUS WREN

BLUEBIRD

14

greenish. Such plumages are frequently mottled and resemble bark, dry grass, gravel, and so forth (depending upon the normal background of the bird). Frequently, plumages have conspicuous bands or streaks of boldly contrasting color such as black or white. These serve to break up the outline of the animal, thus making it difficult to see. Such markings are termed *ruptive*. Many birds have very conspicuous patches of color which have evolved with the function of signalling certain kinds of information to others. These colored areas may be always visible or may only show when the bird erects that portion of the plumage.

Feathers become badly worn with use so that a bird's plumage is periodically replaced by a process called the *molt*. Some species have need, also, of getting rid of conspicuous plumages worn during the breeding season and which become a liability the rest of the year. Normally, feathers are lost and replaced gradually during a definite period at least once a year. Almost all birds replace the entire plumage with a new one after each breeding season. Some birds, in addition, have a complete or partial molt before the breeding season begins. Some birds lose all of their wing feathers at once before getting new ones, for example, many ducks.

Feathers have evolved from reptilian scales and grow from follicles in the skin. They do not ordinarily grow scattered uniformly over the body but only from certain areas termed *feather tracts*. We do not ordinarily see the bare spaces between the feather tracts because the feathers of adjacent tracts overlap.

A typical feather has a central shaft termed the *rachis* from each side of which grow a closely spaced series of *barbs*. The barbs have branching from them a closely spaced series of smaller branches called *barbules*. The barbules, in turn, have a series of even smaller branches termed *barbicels* which have little hooks growing from them termed *ham-*

BARN OWL HAS NEARLY WORLD-WIDE DISTRIBUTION

AFRICAN OSTRICH IS SWIFT RUNNER
AND OMNIVOROUS FEEDER

PEREGRINE FALCON CHASING BLUEJAY

GREAT BLUE HERON

the blue colors found in birds and for the iridescent and shiny effects often seen. The pigments found in feathers are of two main kinds; *lipochromes* and *melanins*. Lipochromes are responsible for the yellows and reds and the melanins are responsible for blacks, browns, reddish browns, and yellowish browns. Green is most commonly formed by yellow lipochrome underlying structures which reflect only blue light. The combination of yellow and blue of course gives green. If you wet a green feather you will destroy temporarily the light reflecting properties of the structures reflecting blue and the feather will appear a dirty yellowish brown. When the feather dries, it will appear green once again.

uli (singular: *hamulus*). These little hooks are responsible for the fact that a mussed feather can be smoothly arranged again by stroking it with the fingers (or a bird's bill during preening). This arrangement helps to assure the extremely light, strong, and flexible nature of feathers so important in flight. Feathers are made of *keratin* which is similar to the material in your own finger nails.

How Birds Get Their Colors

The color of feathers is either due to *pigments* incorporated in the feather structure or to the *microscopic structure* of the feather which allows light of only certain wave lengths to be reflected. These microscopic structures are responsible for most of

RUBY THROATED HUMMINGBIRD FEEDS ON SMALL INSECTS AND FLOWER NECTAR

17

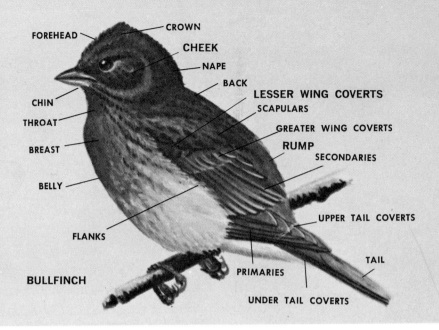

FOREHEAD — CROWN
CHEEK
NAPE
BACK
LESSER WING COVERTS
SCAPULARS
GREATER WING COVERTS
RUMP
SECONDARIES
CHIN
THROAT
BREAST
BELLY
UPPER TAIL COVERTS
FLANKS
TAIL
BULLFINCH
PRIMARIES
UNDER TAIL COVERTS

The feet and bills of birds may also show various colors and patterns. In addition, many birds have various patches of bare skin which may be brightly colored. These features follow the same rules for pattern and color as do plumages. Some of these features may help to render the bird cryptically colored, some may be ruptive, and some may be signals to other birds.

The Skin

The *skin* of birds is typically thin and without glands of any

RELAXED

SLEEKED

FLUFFED

RUFFLED

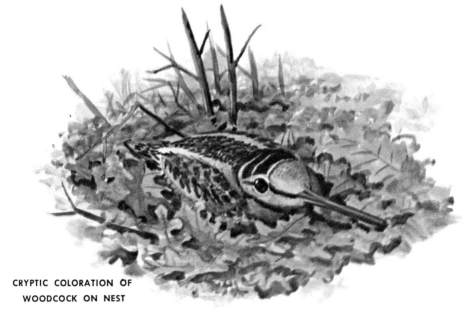

CRYPTIC COLORATION OF
WOODCOCK ON NEST

kind so common among mammals, including ourselves. There are no oil or sweat glands, for instance, scattered over the body. Most birds, however, do have one large gland, the *oil gland* or *uropygial gland* situated on the upper surface immediately in front of the tail. This gland secretes an oily substance which is taken in the bill and distributed over the plumage during preening. As might be expected, this gland is very large and active in water birds. A few birds do not have an oil gland.

The Skeleton

The *skeleton* of a bird is remarkably light and strong and, like all other structural features of birds, is remarkably well adapted for flight. Many of the bones are hollow. Basically, a bird's skeleton is similar to those of other vertebrates, including our own. It serves to support and stiffen the softer anatomical features. Birds have a large but variable number of *vertebrae* making up the neck. This gives the neck great flexibility. On the other

RUPTIVE MARKINGS OF KILLDEER

19

MALE RUFFED GROUSE, ADVERTISING DISPLAY

CORMORANT COURTSHIP DISPLAY

HERRING GULLS FACING AWAY,
AN APPEASEMENT DISPLAY

hand, the vertebrae of the back are largely fused together thus rendering the body quite rigid—another adaptation to flight.

The breast-bone or *sternum* of flying birds is large and has a deep keel necessary for the attachment of large breast muscles used to power the wings. Birds are "high winged monoplanes" with the attendant low center of gravity which gives such planes good stability in flight. Some flightless birds such as the Ostrich do not have a keel on the sternum which is flat and plate-like. Such a sternum is termed *ratite* (raft-like) as opposed to the *carinate* (keeled) types found in flying birds.

Birds typically have four toes, three pointing forward and one to the rear. They have thus lost one toe of the typical vertebrate number of five which we still retain. No bird has more than four toes on each foot although some have three (some woodpeckers) and one, the Ostrich, has but two. Some birds have two toes pointing forward and two backward. Such a foot is called *zygodactyl* and is found in all parrots, cuckoos, woodpeckers, and owls for example.

The arms, of course, have been modified into wings and two fingers have been lost entirely (the "thumb" and "little finger"). The remaining fingers are extensively fused to one another and

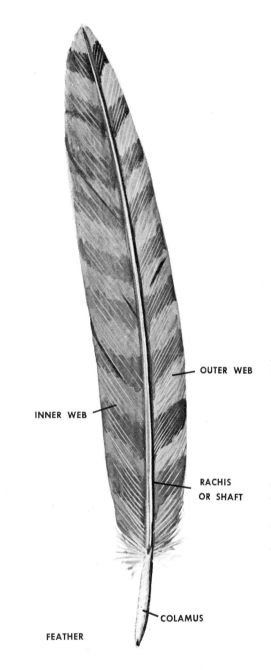

OUTER WEB

INNER WEB

RACHIS OR SHAFT

COLAMUS

FEATHER

elongated to mainly form the "hand" to which the *primary* wing feathers are attached. The fore-arm, composed (as in ourselves) of a *radius* and an *ulna*, support the *secondary* wing feathers. These provide most of the "lift" during flight, the primaries providing the propulsive force. The upper arm contains the *humerus*,

21

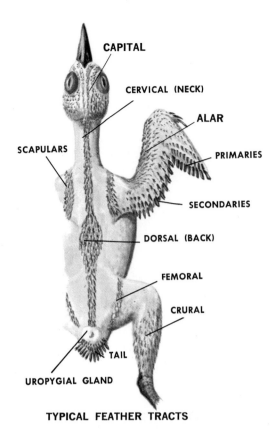

CAPITAL

CERVICAL (NECK)

ALAR

PRIMARIES

SCAPULARS

SECONDARIES

DORSAL (BACK)

FEMORAL

CRURAL

TAIL

UROPYGIAL GLAND

TYPICAL FEATHER TRACTS

last half-dozen or so are fused to-gether, forming the *pygostyle* which supports the tail.

The skull is very light for its size and contains large sockets for the eyes. The jaw bone is hinged to the skull through an interven-ing bone, the *quadrate* (a rep-tilian characteristic). Our jaws hinge directly on the skull. In birds, the bones of the skull are in two thin layers separated by myriads of tiny, bony rods. This makes the skull both strong and light.

The muscles of birds are sim-ilar to those of other vertebrates. The most obvious difference is the presence of the very large breast muscles attached to the sternum.

The Digestive System

The digestive system of birds consists of the mouth cavity, a tube (*esophagus*) connecting the mouth with the *stomach* (which has two parts), the intestines, and associated structures mostly pro-ducing various digestive juices. The first part of the stomach is called the *proventriculus*, a soft organ containing many digestive glands. Immediately behind the proventriculus is the *gizzard*, a heavily muscled organ with an ex-tremely tough lining. Food is ground up in the gizzard aided by bits of gravel which the bird swallows. Many species have a *crop*. This is a thin-walled en-largement of the esophagus in

which is attached, in turn, to the shoulder. From the shoulder grow three important bones, the *scap-ula* or shoulder blade, the *clav-icle* or wish-bone or collar bone, and the *coracoid*. Where these three bones come together at the shoulder they form a hole called the *foramen triosseum* (hole formed by three bones). Through this hole passes a tendon which is attached to the upper surface of the wing. This tendon, is also at-tached to one of the great breast muscles, transmits power to the upper surface of the wing thus lifting it during flight. The bulk of the breast muscles are attached directly to the lower surface of the wing where they supply power for the down-stroke. Birds have very few vertebrae in the tail and the

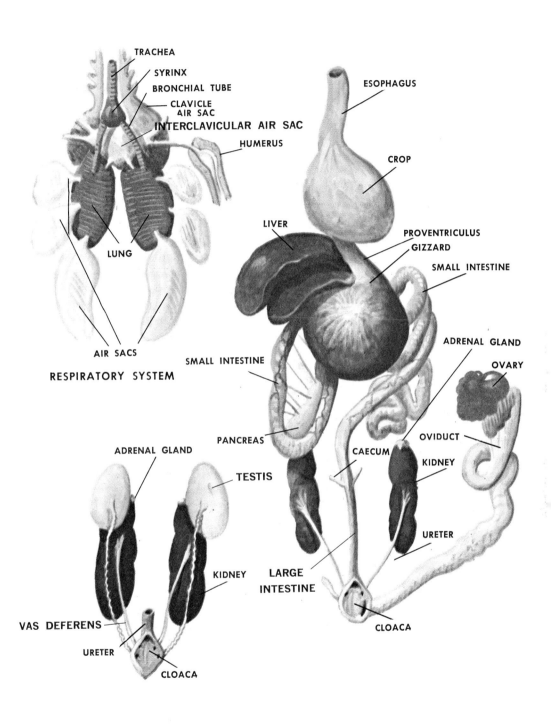

TRACHEA

SYRINX

BRONCHIAL TUBE

CLAVICLE
AIR SAC

INTERCLAVICULAR AIR SAC

HUMERUS

LUNG

AIR SACS

RESPIRATORY SYSTEM

ESOPHAGUS

CROP

LIVER

PROVENTRICULUS

GIZZARD

SMALL INTESTINE

SMALL INTESTINE

PANCREAS

ADRENAL GLAND

OVARY

OVIDUCT

KIDNEY

ADRENAL GLAND

TESTIS

CAECUM

KIDNEY

VAS DEFERENS

URETER

KIDNEY

LARGE
INTESTINE

URETER

CLOACA

CLOACA

DIGESTIVE AND UROGENITAL SYSTEM

23

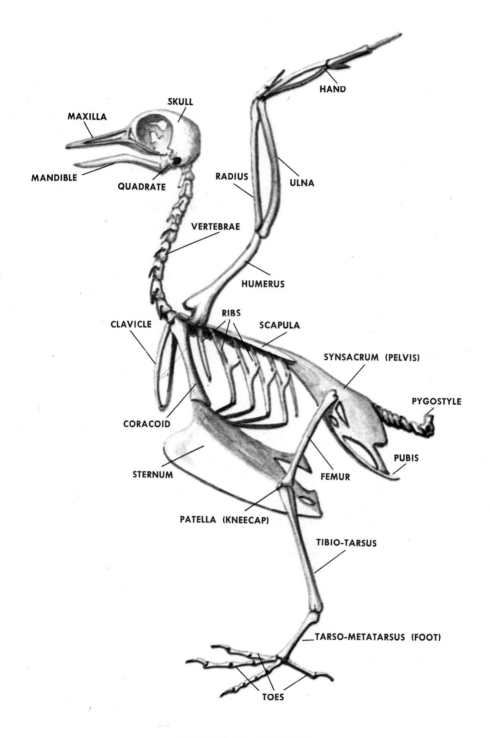

MAXILLA

SKULL

MANDIBLE

QUADRATE

RADIUS

HAND

ULNA

VERTEBRAE

HUMERUS

CLAVICLE

RIBS

SCAPULA

SYNSACRUM (PELVIS)

PYGOSTYLE

CORACOID

STERNUM

PUBIS

FEMUR

PATELLA (KNEECAP)

TIBIO-TARSUS

TARSO-METATARSUS (FOOT)

TOES

SKELETON SYSTEM

which food is temporarily stored before passing along to the stomach. In doves, the crop produces a special fluid termed "pigeon's milk" which is fed to their young. Many other species such as various parrots also feed their young by regurgitation but their crops do not secrete a special substance.

The heavily muscled gizzard is most typical of species which eat hard foods such as grain and nuts. Birds which typically eat mostly softer foods (such as meat, fruit, or nectar) have less heavily muscled gizzards. Some birds which have seasonal shifts in their diets from hard to soft foods, have a corresponding shift in the muscularity of their gizzards. Because of their very high metabolisms, birds must eat prodigious amounts of food. "Eating like a bird" doesn't mean what it is generally supposed to!

Many birds form *pellets* in their stomachs. These are made up of the indigestible portions of their food such as hair, feathers, bones, teeth, fruit pits and so on. These pellets are then ejected from the mouth. This is best known for owls and hawks but it is not so generally known that many small song birds do the same with the hard parts of insects and fruit pits.

After the stomach comes the *small intestine,* then the *large intestine.* Most of the food is digested in the small intestine. Aid-

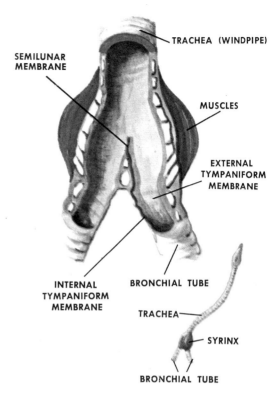

SEMILUNAR MEMBRANE

TRACHEA (WINDPIPE)

MUSCLES

EXTERNAL TYMPANIFORM MEMBRANE

INTERNAL TYMPANIFORM MEMBRANE

BRONCHIAL TUBE

TRACHEA

SYRINX

BRONCHIAL TUBE

CROSS SECTION OF SYRINX

ing digestion are secretions from the *pancreas* and the *liver.* Many birds have *caecae.* These are elongated tubes arising from near where the large and small intestine join and have blind endings. It has been shown, that, in some birds, these caecae aid in the digestion of cellulose. Birds which eat mostly meat, nectar, and other concentrated or more easily digested foods tend to have much shorter intestines than those which eat harder to digest and bulkier foods such as grain, fruit, and other vegetable matter.

The *tongues* of birds are very variable, depending on their diet. Some are thick and fleshy such as those of parrots and some are long,

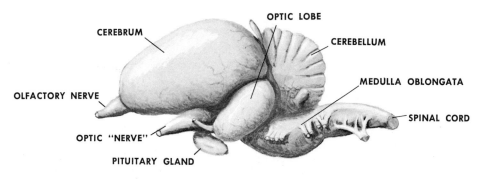

BRAIN OF BIRD

thin and barbed at their tips such as those of some woodpeckers which spear grubs in their wooden tunnels. The tongues of hummingbirds may be tubular. Through these they draw flower nectar. The tongues of most small birds are rather long, flattened, pointed and with a hard, horny tip. *Salivary* and *mucous* glands keep the mouth and tongue moist. Some birds use a special kind of saliva to cement their nests together and one, an Asiatic swift, makes almost its entire nest from hardened saliva. These are the nests from which birds' nest soup is made, a great delicacy to some people.

The Respiratory System

The *respiratory* system of birds is very complicated. Air is breathed in through the nostrils or mouth and passes down the wind-pipe or *trachea*. From here it passes through the *bronchial* tubes to the *lungs*. The lungs of most animals are dead ends in which oxygen is taken from the air for transport by the blood and in which the blood gives up its waste gasses to be exhaled. The lungs serve this function in birds, too, but air can pass all the way through the lungs and into a system of *air sacs*. These sacs extend throughout the body of a bird and

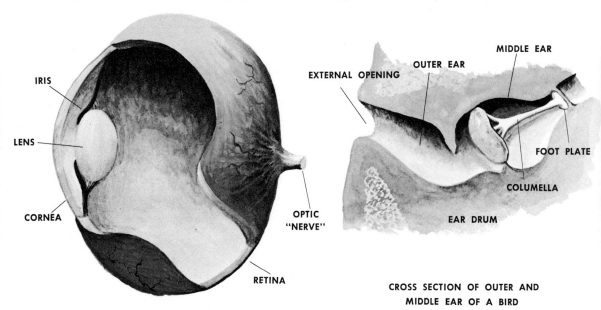

BIRD'S EYE CUT OPEN TO SHOW STRUCTURES

CROSS SECTION OF OUTER AND
MIDDLE EAR OF A BIRD

KIWI PROBING FOR EARTHWORMS

even into some of the hollow bones. These sacs serve to render the bird lighter for their size, thus more buoyant in both air and water. They also serve to help temperature regulation by providing extra evaporating surfaces. Birds do not have a muscular *diaphragm* separating the chest cavity from the abdominal cavity. This, by its movements, helps mammals to breathe. Birds can only cause expansion and contraction of their lungs by moving their ribs and sternum. This occurs automatically during flight as the great breast muscles alternately relax and contract.

How Birds Make Sounds

The *larynx* in birds, unlike that in mammals, is very simple and does not play a part in sound production. Instead, birds produce their vocalizations with the *syrinx*, a complicated structure situated at the base of the trachea. Within the syrinx are several membranes which vibrate with the passage of air over them. The tension on the various membranes is controlled by a set of small muscles, thus enabling the bird to make a variety of sounds. Song birds have the most intricate syringeal muscles and they are capable of producing an astounding array of sounds. Some of these birds can even produce more than one note at a time and vary them independently of one another.

Some birds have elaborate outgrowths of the trachea (many male ducks, for instance) or elaborately coiled tracheas (some swans and cranes) which are probably useful in making their voices more resonant. The air sacs of birds probably also modify the sounds birds make just as do our own head sinuses. Birds breathe much more rapidly than do most animals. A pigeon in flight, for instance, breathes over four hundred times a minute! This is associated with the great activity and high metabolism of birds.

FALCON ATTACKING SWIFT

KINGFISHER DIVING FOR FISH

TURKEY VULTURE WATCHING FOR DEAD ANIMALS

WOODPECKER CHISELING
OPEN INSECT BURROWS

SPARROW (EVENING GROSBEAK) HUSKING SEEDS

PHEASANT SCRATCHING TO UNCOVER FOOD

The Circulatory System

The *circulatory system* of birds is similar to that of mammals in most respects. It provides transportation of the blood. The four chambered *heart* serves as a pump to force freshly oxygenated blood throughout the body and waste laden blood through the lungs and kidneys. The *aorta*, the large artery carrying blood from the heart to the body, curves over to the right in birds instead of to the left as in mammals.

As might be expected, the heart beats very rapidly in birds. Of course, the rate varies greatly from species to species and with the amount of activity. It may beat less than one hundred times a minute to over a thousand times a minute!

Body temperatures may also vary among species. Some may be around 100 degrees Fahrenheit, but most are higher, being well over this figure.

Reproduction

The *urogenital system* consists of the kidneys and *reproductive organs*. These are treated together because they are closely associated both functionally and structurally. Birds have two kidneys, each of which has three lobes. Kidneys filter certain waste products from the blood. This is excreted as semi-liquid uric acid, rather than urea as in most mammals. The whitish portion of bird droppings consists of these kidney wastes. These wastes are secreted into the lower large intestine called the *cloaca*.

Like mammals, male birds have two *testes* which produce sperm cells. The testes lie against the back near the kidneys. Unlike female mammals, however, most female birds have but one functional *ovary* instead of two. The ovary produces *egg follicles*.

TOWHEE SCRATCHING TO UNCOVER FOOD

29

HOUSE WREN DRINKING

When an egg follicle leaves the ovary it enters a long tube called the *oviduct*. The oviduct has different functions at various places along its length. The egg follicle is fertilized by a sperm cell near its upper end. The fertilized egg gets a thick layer of *albumen* or egg white about half way down the oviduct. Further along, the shell is added and it is here that pigment is incorporated if the egg is to be colored. Most birds lay an egg every day until the clutch is completed, but others may lay only every other day as do some parrots and owls, for instance.

Some birds do not incubate their eggs until all have been laid, all the young then hatch at about the same time. Other birds begin incubating with the first egg laid. This results in the young hatching at intervals so that there is a graded size series in each nest. Among such birds are parrots, owls, and hawks, for example.

The oviduct and sperm ducts also enter the cloaca before the outside is reached.

The Nervous System

The *nervous system* of birds is similar to that of other vertebrates. It is composed of the *brain, spinal cord,* and *peripheral nerves* and functions to receive sensory input which is then referred to various muscles and glands for appropriate action. The brain of birds is noted for its very small *olfactory lobes* (associated with the sense of smell), large optic lobes (associated with sight), a rather large but smooth *cerebrum*

MOURNING DOVE DRINKING

(the cerebrum is usually fissured in mammals where it is mostly associated with learned behavior), a rather well-developed *cerebellum* (associated with precise control over movements), and the *medulla oblongata* (mainly responsible for involuntary movements of muscles such as the heart).

Important Glands

A very important gland, the *pituitary,* is located at the base of the brain. This gland has many important functions and is often referred to as the "master gland" since its activities figure prominently in so many bodily functions. It secretes *gonadotropic* hormones which are responsible for stimulating the production of both male hormones (*androgens*) and female hormones (*estrogens*). Also, it produces *lactogenic* hormone (*prolactin*) which stimulates the production of "pigeon's milk," for instance. In addition, the pituitary helps regulate egg-laying, affects parental behavior,

and stimulates the *adrenal* glands (located near the kidneys).

The adrenal glands produce hormones which are associated with helping the body set up defenses against shock and other stresses. The *thyroid* gland, located in the base of the neck, is also at least partly controlled by the pituitary and is associated with proper molting, development of the sexual organs, temperature regulation, and proper metabolism. The *islets of Langerhans* in the pancreas is responsible for secreting a hormone necessary for proper sugar metabolism. It is one gland *not* under the influence of the pituitary. All of these glands are called *endocrine* glands and work by secreting their hormones into the blood stream where they are carried to their appropriate "target organs" which are usually in the central nervous system. Here, they stimulate an appropriate nervous response which in turn initiates some appropriate internal or external action on the part of the bird.

ROBIN ON NEST THREATENING FINGER

The Sense Organs

The *sense organs* of birds are responsible for receiving information from the environment. The most important sense organs of birds, like ourselves, are the *eyes* and *ears*. The eyes of birds are very well developed and are capable, as far as we know, of seeing different colors. In addition, they are able to focus quickly and very sharply on both near and far objects. Most birds have *monocular* vision. That is, they see a completely different view from each eye since they are typically located on opposite sides of the head. However, owls, with their forward directed eyes, have *binocular* vision much as we do. They see much the same view from both eyes. Many birds are able to use both types of vision by moving their eyes. There is much variability in this and it depends upon the kind of life to which each kind of bird is adapted.

The ears of birds are quite sensitive but, in general, tend to be less sensitive than our ears to lower pitched sounds. However, they generally have very good hearing in the higher ranges of sounds. A bird's ears are located on each side of its head, usually a little behind and below the eyes. Since most birds do not have external ear flaps as we do, it is difficult to see their ear openings because they are hidden by feathers. They are easy to see, however, in very young birds before they get their feathers or in birds with naked heads such as many vultures. Birds have but one bone, a slender rod called the *columella,* connecting the ear drum or *tympanum* with the inner ear where the nerve endings of the *auditory* nerve are. The auditory nerve transmits impulses to the brain where they are interpreted as sounds. You may remember that, unlike birds, we have three little bones in our middle ears instead of one.

32

Carnivores: Sparrow Hawk and Burrowing Owl with hooked bills.

Mud sifter: Roseate Spoonbill with spatulate bill.

VARIATION IN
BIRDS

The following pictures represent a very small sample of the wonderful adaptive diversity found among birds. Each of the variations in shape, color, pattern, size, and behavior represent genetic responses to environmental selective pressures. These pressures affect the probability of survival of each individual in a population. Those individuals best constituted for survival tend to survive, thus passing their characteristics to the next generation. The major source of the necessary individual variation is the constant recombination of genetic material afforded by sexual reproduction. This, coupled with selective pressures applied by an ever changing environment over very long periods of time, results in the diversity encountered.

Seed eater: Evening Grosbeak cracking sunflower seed.

Nectar eater: Anna's Hummingbird about to sip nectar from trumpet creeper.

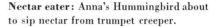

VARIATION IN BIRDS' TOES

Long toes of Marsh bird: Purple Gallinule

Climbing toes of Woodpecker (2 front, 2 behind): Gilded Flicker

Webbed toes: Wood Duck

Normal foot of perching bird (3 front, 1 behind): Blue Jay

VARIATIONS IN BIRDS' WINGS

Rounded wing: Palmer Thrasher

Pointed wing: Barn Swallow

Square wing: Gila Woodpecker

Long, narrow wing: Black Skimmer

BIRD ACTIVITIES

Drinking: Cardinal

Preening: Killdeer

Bathing: Gambel's Sparrows

Resting and sleeping: Mallards on ice

Fighting reflection in mirror: Song Sparrow

Courting "Grunt whistle": Mallard

Drumming: Ruffed Grouse

Displaying: Wild Turkey

VARIATIONS IN BIRDS' NESTS

Roofed over — ground nest: Meadowlark

Cottony nest: Yellow Warbler

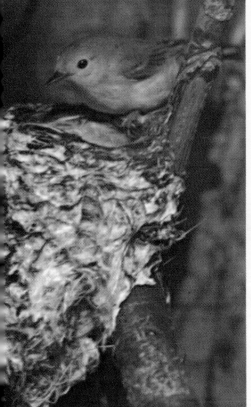

Simple depression in ground: Killdeer

Hanging nest: Blue-headed Vireo

Long distance migrant: Golden
Plover

Scarlet Tanager family

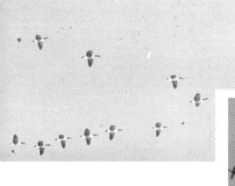

Migrating V: Canada Geese

Assembling for migration: Bank
Swallows

ATTRACTING BIRDS

Evening Grosbeaks at window
shelf feeder.

White-breasted Nuthatch on birdhouse.

Birdhouse for Purple Martins.

Painted Bunting at automatic
feeder.

The *sense of touch* is generally rather poorly developed in birds but some have nerve endings associated with touch in their bills or at feather bases.

The *sense of taste* in birds is generally poorer than our own but there is much variability among different species. Parrots have quite a few taste buds in their mouths but in many birds they are rare.

The *sense of smell* is even poorer in birds. You have already learned that their olfactory lobes are poorly developed and other anatomical features associated with smell are also poorly developed. Vultures and other birds which eat carrion probably locate it by sight alone. When such food is hidden from view, they probably rely upon the visual detection of flies and other insects associated with dead animals. An exception to the poor sense of smell in birds are the strange kiwis of New Zealand. These long-billed birds probe about in the soil at night, feeding upon earthworms. Their anatomical features associated with smell are quite well developed and their nostrils, unlike those of other birds, are located near the tip of their bills.

Other senses such as those of pain, pressure, heat, cold, and so forth are poorly known for birds. We can assume, however, from observational evidence, that birds possess these to some extent, at least.

BIRD OF PARADISE DISPLAYING

PENGUIN "FLYING" UNDERWATER

THE BEHAVIOR OF BIRDS

Now that we know something about the structures of birds we can find out how they use these structures. Birds, like other animals, inherit their behavior patterns just as they do their feathers, eyes, or muscles. This means, of course, that all behavior has a genetic basis. However, some behaviors are inherited more "directly" and others more "indirectly." Indirect inheritance refers to the fact that some behavior patterns have to be learned through experiences the animal has during its life but the ability to do this is inherited. Many complex behaviors that birds have are a result of a combination of both methods of acquiring behavior. The same can be said of struc-

tures. We, for instance, directly inherit a biceps muscle in our arm. However, by subjecting this muscle to certain experiences we can, within genetically determined limits, cause it to become larger and more powerful or smaller and weaker than it would have been otherwise. We can "teach" our biceps to become different by giving it different experiences just as we can teach an animal to change its behavior within inherited limitations.

Directly inherited behavior is commonly called *instinctive* or *innate* behavior. Indirectly inherited behavior is usually termed *learned* behavior. There seems to be many borderline cases and much has to be found out before

ROUNDED WINGS, SHORT TAIL (RUFFED GROUSE)

LONG POINTED WINGS AND TAIL OF PASSENGER PIGEON

**ROUNDED WINGS, LONG TAIL
(SHARP-SHINNED HAWK)**

we thoroughly understand the behavior of any animal, including ourselves.

The behaviors that birds and other animals have can be roughly divided into two groups. One group includes all the behaviors associated with keeping alive and healthy. These behaviors are called *maintenance activities*. The other group of behaviors are concerned with reproducing the species and are termed *reproductive activities*. There is overlap in these two groups because a dead or unhealthy animal cannot reproduce but the division is still a useful one.

A biologist asks the same four basic questions of a behavior as he does of a structure. He wants to know its *function* (what it does for the animal), *biological significance* (how it affects the probability of survival), *causation* (what internal and external conditions are necessary), and its *evolution* (what is the evolutionary history of the behavior).

Keeping alive and healthy involves many different kinds of behavior. Some of these are feeding; drinking; keeping warm, dry, clean and keeping the plumage neatly arranged; escaping enemies; resting; and simply moving. Except for keeping the plumage arranged properly, these things must all be accomplished by ourselves also.

What Birds Eat

A great variety of animal and vegetable foods are consumed by birds and an even greater variety of methods have evolved with the function of finding, preparing, and eating such foods. Some; such as many hawks, owls, herons, and storks; kill their own animal food as do small insect-eating birds. Some of these may actively chase their prey and capture it in midflight as do falcons, swallows, swifts, and nighthawks. Others

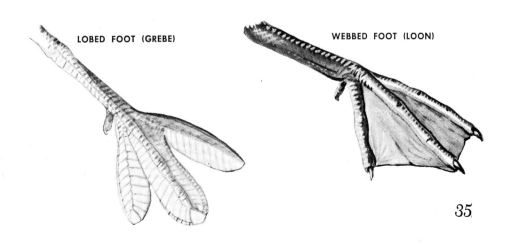

LOBED FOOT (GREBE)   WEBBED FOOT (LOON)

may sit quietly and wait for their prey to come near enough to be seized. Among such birds are some birds of prey and herons. In all cases vision plays an important part. Robins run about our lawns in search of earthworms which they see (not hear) and then seize and pull from their burrows. Woodpeckers chisel into the wooden tunnels of wood-boring insects and extract them with specially adapted tongues. The variety of methods of capturing animal food is almost endless and extends from the complex searching and capturing behavior of a hunting falcon to the simple, patient waiting of vultures which circle high in the sky until they see a dead animal upon which to descend and feed. Kingfishers may dive into the water for fish as do many aquatic birds such as gannets, pelicans, and terns. Others may wait patiently for prey to come by as do many flycatchers, bluebirds, bee-eaters, and shrikes.

Birds may eat seeds of various sizes including large, hard nuts; various fruits; tender plant shoots, and other plant material. Some are narrowly adapted to eat only a limited variety of foods and some may eat a wide variety. Others may eat both animal and plant foods. Those eating seeds are called *gramnivorous*, those eating fruit are called *frugivorous*, and those eating meat are called *carnivorous* if they eat other vertebrates or *insectivorous* if they eat insects. Animals which eat both plant and animal foods are called *omnivorous*.

Some birds take the husks from the seeds they eat before they swallow them. Different species have different ways of doing this. Some swallow seeds whole without first husking them. Fruit-eating birds may bite bits from fruit or swallow them whole, depending mostly upon the size.

THREATENING
ABYSSINIAN LOVEBIRD

SUBMISSIVE GOLDFINCH

Some birds will only eat seeds contained in the pods or heads and others will scratch about on the ground for seeds which have fallen there. Some such birds scratch with only one leg at a time as do pheasants and quail, for example, but others may scratch with both legs at once as do many ·sparrows. So deeply rooted is this scratching that many species will scratch while feeding even though they are standing in a pile of uncovered seeds. Other species may use their bills to uncover food. They may flip their bills sideways to do this or they may flip them straight out in front.

All birds *drink* water. Some need more than do others. Birds which live in deserts either have evolved in such a way that they need very little water (Budgerigars, for instance) or they periodically fly long distances to water holes (sandgrouse, for instance). Most birds drink, as do chickens, by dipping the bill in the water and then raising the head high to let the water flow down the esophagus. A few birds such as pigeons, sandgrouse, and some finches drink by keeping the bill in the water and forcing the water down their throats by a series of pumping actions. Many sea birds are able to drink salt water. The excess salt is then secreted by special glands in the head, the excreted salt running from their nostrils.

How Birds Adapt to Climate

We have already discussed how birds may adjust their feathers in order to adjust their temperatures and how the air sacs, through evaporation, may help cool them. To make this easier,

SUBMISSIVE ABYSSINIAN LOVEBIRD

most birds will pant with open bill when excessively warm. Birds will also seek shelter from rain and snow. They also seek shade during the hottest part of the day if they are becoming too warm. Some birds will huddle together, particularly at night, to keep warm. Bobwhite Quail and Brown Creepers will do this, for instance. Birds have a dense network of small blood vessels near the surface in the arm-pit or *axillary* region. When too warm, many will raise their wings out from the body, exposing this region thus helping to cool the blood.

As mentioned before, a well-kept plumage is quite waterproof and if most birds are not exposed to water too long they will not become wet. Water birds, of course, have the best waterproofing but even these will become soaked and tend to sink if they do not frequently preen and oil their feathers. Ducks usually come to land for this but many water birds

BLACK MASKED LOVEBIRDS PAIR FOR LIFE

such as grebes and loons may preen and oil their feathers while in the water. These will even roll over on their backs in order to preen the belly.

How Birds Keep Clean

The plumage is kept neat and in place by *preening*. The bill takes hold of the feather and strokes it from base to tip much as we would smooth out a mussed feather between our fingers. Birds also remove the old, dry feather sheaths from newly grown feathers with their bills. Birds keep clean by bathing in water, by preening away dirt, and by ruffling and shaking the plumage much in the way a wet dog dries itself. Some birds will bathe in snow if water is not available. Others will bathe in dust as do chickens and English Sparrows. Exactly how this helps the birds is not clear. Many birds will sun bathe. They ruffle the plumage and let the sun shine on their ex-

SAGE GROUSE (VISUAL ADVERTISING)

posed skin. The function of this is not known but, at least in some birds, it may help to furnish them with vitamin D. The exact way in which birds preen, bathe, dry themselves, and scratch varies from species to species. Much more knowledge is needed about these things.

Birds clean their bills by wiping them against perches. Some use scrubbing motions and others strop first on one side and then on the other. They scratch their heads with their feet. Some birds scratch by bringing a foot forward *over* the wing and some do it by bringing the foot forward *under* the wing. Most large birds scratch under the wing and most small birds do it the other way but there are many exceptions and some even change methods with their age.

The Enemies of Birds

The enemies of birds are many. They may be other birds; reptiles such as snakes, lizards, and turtles; and mammals. Even frogs and large spiders have been known to catch and eat birds! In addition there are, of course, various internal and external parasites as well as diseases.

They protect themselves from animals which might prey upon them by fleeing, fighting back, or by hiding. Behavior which has to do with attack and escape behavior is termed *agonistic* behavior. This may be very elaborate in some birds, particularly those which fight others of their own kind over mates, nest-sites, and so forth. Birds which are particularly swift on the wing usually flee from their enemies. Those which are cryptically colored will often try to hide but will flee or attack if discovered. Birds which have potent weapons such as owls, hawks, or parrots will often effectively defend themselves. Most birds will defend themselves the best way they can if they are prevented from fleeing. A bird may not be able to flee because he is already caught or because of a strong conflicting behavior preventing fleeing such as parental care behavior in birds with eggs or young.

ORDINARY SLEEPING POSTURE
(ROSE-BREASTED GROSBEAK)

Any external parasites (lice, ticks, fleas) are picked off with the bill or scratched off with a foot. Internal parasites are more difficult to get rid of but a normal, healthy bird usually is not excessively bothered by them. Their only defense against disease is their possible immunity and, possibly, in some birds, by not living too close together.

How Birds Sleep

Birds spend much time resting during the day and sleeping at night. Most prepare for sleep by fluffing the plumage (to keep warm) and tucking the head into the feathers of the back and shoulder (not under the wing!). There are other sleeping postures. For instance toucans fold their heads over their backs and their tails toward the head. Some birds (African colies and Asiatic hanging parrakeets, for example) sleep by hanging upside down. Birds may sleep with one or both feet on the perch. There is a special foot mechanism which grips the perch tighter automatically as the bird relaxes in sleep so that the feet can not allow the bird to fall.

Birds in Motion

Different kinds of birds are adapted for different kinds of flying and some do not fly at all. Among these are the penguins of the antarctic whose wings have become flippers for swimming underwater and the great running birds such as the Ostrich, Emu, Cassowaries, and Rheas. The kiwis, mentioned earlier, can not fly either. There are also birds which can not fly but which belong to groups of birds which can. Among these are flightless cormorants, rails, and grebes. Many birds can fly but do so very poorly such as some South American tinamous. Some birds are adapted for swift flights of short duration. All of these have short, rounded wings. Among these are grouse, pheasants, and many small birds. Birds which are capable of long

UPSIDE DOWN SLEEPING
(RED-FACED LOVEBIRD)

PLOVER NEST   TERN NEST

distance flights at high speeds have long, pointed wings. Among such birds are falcons, swifts, and pigeons. Birds which spend much time soaring on almost motionless wings tend to have rather broad, long wings such as those of vultures, storks, some hawks, and eagles. Birds which are highly maneuverable in flight tend to have longer tails than their relatives which are not.

Birds progress on the ground by using their legs. Some *hop* as do many small birds such as most sparrows, some thrushes, jays, and most warblers. Others *walk* as do pheasants, grouse, parrots, pigeons, herons, storks, cranes, blackbirds, and many others. Some are capable of hopping up tree trunks. Woodpeckers do this and are prevented from slipping back by the stiffened, pointed tail feathers. Many birds are extremely awkward on land because their legs are so far back on their bodies. Grebes, for instance, may merely shove themselves along on their bellies when out of water. Many birds swim and dive with great ability. These birds either have *webbed* toes such as those of ducks, loons, pelicans, and gulls or they have *lobed* toes such as those of grebes, coots, and phalaropes.

How Birds Fly

The ways in which the wings of birds actually work during flight are very complicated. They do not simply beat up and down nor do they row the bird through the air as one would row a boat. Actually, the wings of most birds, during flapping flight, beat upward and backward and downward and forward. At the same time, the hand (bearing the primary feathers) executes a sort of sculling motion which provides power. A cross section of a bird's wing is very much like that of an airplane's. The leading edge is rather blunt, becoming thicker for a short distance, and then progressively thinner out to the trailing edge. In addition, the wing is "cambered." That is, the wing is slightly curved in section so that the bottom surface is concave while the upper surface is convex. This camber, coupled with the characteristic cross section shape, is a common feature of airfoils and it is this shape that causes air to flow over the wing

41

BLACK DUCK NEST WITH THICK DOWN LINING

FAIRY TERN LAYS ITS SINGLE EGG ON TREE BRANCH

in such a way that a partial vacuum tends to form over the upper surface. This is what provides the lift that keeps the bird (or airplane) in the air.

Drag must be kept to a minimum. Some drag is caused by the friction of air against the bird but the most serious drag may be caused by air turbulence as it flows past the wing edges. Airplanes use a system of slots and flaps in the wings to reduce drag and birds often have such slots near the tips of their wings.

Notice the slots at the wing tips of the soaring Turkey Vulture in the picture. Soaring birds, to be efficient, must have as little drag as possible. Humming birds fly much as do helicopters. The direction of flight and speed is determined by the pitch of the wings and the speed of their movement.

CROSS SECTION OF WOODPECKER NEST

POINTED EGG OF MURRE LAID ON NARROW LEDGE

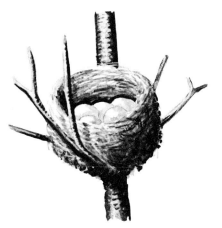

CUP NEST OF GOLDFINCH

BAG-LIKE NEST OF BALTIMORE ORIOLE

The Fighting "Language" of Birds

Fighting is mostly biologically disadvantageous because one or both contestants risk being seriously injured or killed. This is certainly incompatible with staying alive and healthy and also with reproduction! To avoid actual fighting and yet retain the advantages of fighting (securing mates, nest-sites, food and so forth) most birds and other animals have evolved a more or less elaborate *threat* system. These threats tend to be most elaborate and effective in those species which are capable of doing the most damage to one another.

Birds which are less capable, under ordinary circumstances, of damaging one another usually have less effective and elaborate threat behavior. You would see doves actually fighting much more frequently than you would see eagles doing the same thing. Many countries which use a dove as a symbol of peace may be more accurate than they ever intended!

Most threats consist of stylized incomplete movements to bite, move toward the opponent, or to strike with the feet, or wings. These movements are often enhanced by ruffled or fluffed plumage which frequently has bright

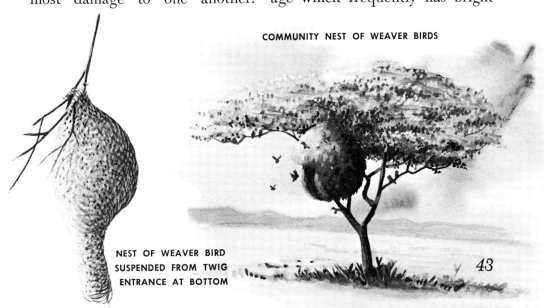

COMMUNITY NEST OF WEAVER BIRDS

NEST OF WEAVER BIRD
SUSPENDED FROM TWIG
ENTRANCE AT BOTTOM

43

or contrasting patches of color showing especially well at these times. Most species have several such threat behaviors, each one indicating a certain probability that an attack will be forthcoming. The weakest such signals say, "I will not bother you unless you come closer." The strongest say, "I will attack immediately if you do not indicate you are beaten." You can see from this that birds have a kind of threat "language" with which they are able to say fairly definite things. Sometimes vocalizations are associated with such threats. Some birds may also snap the bill, hiss, or rattle their feather quills together. Any behavior which has evolved with the express function of communicating information is termed a *display*. Birds have displays other than those of attack and escape. Many have to do with attracting mates, stimulating mates, luring enemies from their nests or young, and indicating the presence of food or predators. Some indicate submission. These are frequently just the opposite of what the same bird would do when threatening. If a bird points his opened bill at the opponent when threatening, he is likely to point his closed bill away if he wants to say, "You have won," or "I am peaceful." If a bird stands tall and sleeked when aggressive the chances are that it will become short and fluffed when submissive.

"Courtship" and Mating

Pair Formation in birds is often very complicated. There are two major problems that must be solved. One is to find a mate and the other is to be sure it is of the right species before eggs are fertilized. In most species, it is the male which takes the initiative. He usually stations himself in an appropriate habitat for his species and *advertises* his presence. He may do this visually or vocally. Many birds employ a combination of these methods. Birds which live in places where the visibility is poor (woods, tall grass, thick brush, etc.) generally rely most heavily on vocal advertising. This is also true of birds which are mainly active at night such as owls. Birds which live in the open tend to rely more heavily upon visual advertising. In addition to vocal sounds, many birds advertise with sounds produced in other ways. Some of these are drumming on dead wood (many woodpeckers), drumming the air with wings (Ruffed Grouse), or letting the wind whistle through specially modified flight feathers (snipe and Woodcock). Most of the bird songs with which you are familiar are advertisements. Visual advertising displays occur in great variety among birds. These displays often employ stylized locomotory movements and the erection of various parts of the plumage

ALTRICIAL YOUNG PARROT

which are often conspicuously patterned and colored. Many advertising displays serve the double function of attracting unpaired females and warning away rival males.

When a female finally joins a male there is often an elaborate set of signals which they give to one another. This insures that both birds belong to the same species before events proceed any further. The length of time the male and female associate with one another varies greatly. Some birds only associate a few hours or minutes—just long enough to fertilize the eggs. Among such birds are hummingbirds, grouse, turkeys, many manakins, and birds of paradise. On the other hand, some form pairs which last for the life of one of the partners. Among such birds are geese, swans, parrots, and some birds of prey. Many birds form pairs which last for just one breeding season. Among these are many of our familiar song birds.

Once a mate has been found of the right species, the next problem is to have both partners *stimulated sufficiently* and at the *same time* so that the eggs can be fertilized. This is usually accomplished by the male performing another elaborate series of visual and vocal displays which stimulates the female. The male is usually stimulated in turn by what the female does and by his own activities.

Birds lay their eggs in a great variety of places. Some merely lay their eggs on the ground with hardly any preparation at all except perhaps a shallow depression which is first scraped out. The eggs of such birds are usually colored to match their backgrounds. Birds which nest in this way include many sandpipers, plovers, and nighthawks. Other ground nesting birds build nests first. These may be quite simple; just a few sticks, straws, and feathers upon which the eggs are

PRECOCIAL YOUNG GOOSE

laid. Among such birds are gulls and terns. More complicated ground nests may be built by ducks, geese, cranes, and others, including many small birds. Birds which lay their eggs on cliff ledges frequently do not build nests but their eggs are often very pointed at one end and broad at the other so that they will roll around themselves rather than off the ledge if they are disturbed. One bird, the Fairy Tern, balances its single egg on the bare branch of a tree! Penguins often nest on bare ice! The egg is incubated by holding it on top of their webbed feet and covering it with a special flap of skin from the abdomen.

Some birds lay their eggs at the bottom of holes they dig in tree trunks (for example, many woodpeckers). Others lay their eggs at the bottom of natural cavities or those which have been dug by other birds (for example, many parrots, chickadees, some wrens, some owls, and bluebirds). Most of these birds do not build nests in these cavities, simply laying their eggs on the bottom of the cavity. Some, such as a few parrots, wrens, and bluebirds, do build nests in the cavities.

A few species tunnel into banks of earth to make their nests. Among these are many kingfishers, Bank Swallows, bee-eaters, and motmots. Other birds, such as many grebes, build nests which float in the water, anchor-ing them to vegetation growing out of the water.

Birds which build their nests in bushes or trees may make cup-shaped structures (for example, warblers, tanagers, gold-finches, jays, crows, herons, and many hawks). Some such birds, however, build very skimpy platforms through the bottoms of which the eggs can often be seen! Some cuckoos and doves are examples of such birds. Other birds nesting off the ground may build bag-like nests suspended from twigs. A good example is our familiar Baltimore Oriole. Other suspended nests may be very elaborate, being completely closed over and having a long entrance tube. Many African and Asiatic weaver finches build such nests. Some South American oven-birds build large hollow balls of mud with an entrance on the side. These are very strong when dry. One species of parrot from South America (Quaker Parrot) and some African weaver-finches build enormous community nests in trees. These "apartment houses" have a separate entrance and nest-ing chamber for each pair of birds.

Nests are commonly built by females but, in some species, the males may help. In a few species, the male alone builds the nest.

Once the eggs are laid, they must be *incubated*. To do this either the male or female sits on the eggs. In many species, the male and female alternate incubation. For instance, in many doves, the female incubates during the night and the male during the day. Other species may change places more frequently. Many species develop a special bare skin area on the breast at this time (*brood patch*). This bare area is especially rich in blood vessels, making it easier to keep the eggs warm. Some of the mound-builders of Australia and adjacent areas do not incubate their eggs at all. The males of these birds rake together huge piles of vegetation in which the females lay their eggs. The heat from the decomposing material warms the eggs. Some birds which nest in very hot places such as on tropical beaches or in deserts, shade their eggs by standing over them rather than incubating them. Some eggs hatch in a few days and others may take over a month. The eggs of most small birds hatch in from eight to twelve days.

Caring for the Young

When the young hatch they may be either *altricial* (quite helpless at first and requiring prolonged *parental care*) or they may be *precocial* (able to run about as soon as their down dries and require much less parental care). Young Robins, canaries, parrakeets, and starlings are altricial. Young chickens, geese, ducks,

EASTERN GOLDEN PLOVER BREEDS IN ARCTIC AND WINTERS IN SOUTHERN SOUTH AMERICA

grouse, and sandpipers, are precocial.

Altricial young may be fed by either parent or both. Precocial young are usually taken care of by the mother only, but there are exceptions.

The young may be dependent upon their parents for very long periods (California Condor) or may be completely independent from hatching (mound-builders). Most young are dependent for three or four weeks. They then may either leave and go their own way or may remain with their parents as a family group for months (geese, for instance).

Most altricial young are fed by food being thrust down their

SCARLET TANAGER SPENDS
SUMMER IN EASTERN UNITED STATES,
WINTER IN NORTHERN SOUTH AMERICA

ulation in young birds is poor for some time and they become easily chilled. Sitting on young to keep them warm is called *brooding*.

Nesting and Breeding

Some birds nest once a year, others more than once a year, and some nest only every other year or so. Most birds breed for the first time the year after they hatch. Others may not breed for several years and some may be able to breed a few weeks after hatching.

Many birds nest as solitary pairs while others are highly social and may nest in colonies of great size. Most of our familiar song birds are solitary nesters. Some colonies of birds exist because the things that they need for living are concentrated in a small area, thus forcing the birds to all live in a small area. For example, some colonies of parrots are like this. Parrots need a cavity in which to nest and if there happens to be many cavities crowded together in a small area of woodland, there may be many pairs of parrots living close to one another. On the other hand, there are some colonial birds that live this way because they have evolved to do so. These birds are dependent upon one another for protection against enemies, and may be dependent upon one another for stimulation (through their vocal and visual displays) to breed. A good example of this

throats by the parents. Some of these young have elaborate colors and patterns in their mouth linings. These make it easier for the parents to feed them, providing a convenient "target." Some young (certain weaver-finches) even have luminous patches around their mouths. These birds nest in dark places and this would certainly make it easier to feed them. Most precocial young are able to pick up their own food, the mother merely taking them to places where food is available, providing them with warmth, and protecting them from predators. Both kinds of young are kept warm by their parents because temperature regis the common parrakeet or Budgerigar. In the wild, these live in very large flocks and breed close together. Single pairs have a very difficult time breeding if they do at all. Every commercial breeder of these birds knows this and keeps many pairs together where they can see and hear one another.

How Birds Find Their Way Home

Birds find their way around in familiar surroundings by learning the position of familiar landmarks. How birds find their way over great distances has puzzled people since ancient times. Birds which find themselves a little way outside familiar areas may search at random in ever widening patterns until they find a familiar landmark. We now know that birds which periodically travel great distances may navigate with the aid of the sun and stars. Just how this is done is very complicated and only partly understood at present.

Many birds living in the Northern Hemisphere migrate long distances every fall to places in the world where living is easier. They return every spring, often to the very spot where they lived the year before. These migrations are not carried out primarily to escape the cold weather. They generally are to insure an adequate food supply. Most birds can

RANGE OF NON-MIGRATORY SAGE

stand considerable cold but would soon die if they did not have enough to eat to maintain their high metabolisms. Many kinds of foods are simply not available during the winter or the days are too short to allow the birds to find and eat a sufficient amount to last through the long cold nights.

Many tropical birds, in particular, are sedentary and do not leave the small area in which they were hatched. Some birds may perform local migrations. Among these are birds that breed at high altitudes in mountains and then descend to the lower valleys for the winter. Some quail do this and they perform these migrations mostly on foot. Some kinds of birds are notorious, not for migrations, but for rather unpredictable wanderings, sometime over great distances. Among these are finches such as the crossbills, redpolls, and Pine Grosbeak.

49

USES OF BIRDS

Aside from the production of fertilizer mentioned before, birds have many uses to man. Most of us enjoy eating chickens, ducks, geese, turkeys and eggs. Birds thus provide us with some of our most delicious foods and some of the species less commonly used for food are squabs (young pigeons), pheasants, and guinea fowl. Most of this meat and eggs comes from domesticated birds kept in captivity. Many people and institutions keep captive birds for other reasons. Swans, ducks, geese, peacocks, and pheasants lend beauty to many parks and lakes. Parakeets, canaries, finches, parrots, and other captive birds are kept as pets for their beauty, interesting ways, or attractive voices. A great many people derive much pleasure in looking for wild birds. Some are merely interested in seeing how many different species they can identify. Others, are curious also about how they live. Many people obtain great enjoyment in photographing birds in their natural habitats. This is a challenging hobby and requires great skill as a bird watcher as well as a photographer.

Many scientists study birds in order to increase man's basic understanding of many problems. They carry out their investigations both in the wild and in the laboratory. Some of the kinds of things studied are evolution, anatomy, behavior (ethology and psychology), physiology, genetics, ecology, and diseases. Understanding any of these topics better increases our understanding of ourselves and permits us to behave more intelligently toward each other and toward our environment. A scientist who is primarily concerned with studying birds is called an *ornithologist*.

You can now see that birds are valuable because they furnish us with meat, eggs, feathers (for sleeping bags and quilts) and fertilizer. They furnish sport for those who like to hunt. They make delightful pets which appeal to our eyes and ears. They furnish scientists with material from which to discover a great many things that will help us to live fuller and healthier lives.

If you would like to watch

TALKING MYNA, POPULAR CAGE BIRD

SWAN ON PARK POND

birds, all that you really need is a place where there are birds and a lot of patience. Wild birds are usually frightened, as you might be, of sudden movements or sudden sounds. It is helpful to have a good pair of binoculars and a notebook in which you should keep information if you are a serious student.

Anyone with a sincere interest and a little patience can make important contributions to our knowledge of birds. The kinds of things we need to know can only come from careful watching of the details of their behavior. For instance, we need to know exactly how they scratch, preen, bathe, drink, and sleep. We need to know exactly how they threaten one another and attract their mates. We would like to know exactly what they eat and feed their young and how they make their nests. All of these things, and more, are needed in great *detail*. One would have to watch many individuals doing the same thing over a considerable period of time and this can only be done by those with enough interest, attention to fine detail, and patience.

Birds can be attracted to our homes by providing things that they need. Chief among these are food, protection against enemies, shelter, and nesting places. Feeding stations can be placed where they are easily seen and protected from cats and other predators. Various shrubs can be planted which provide food, shelter, and protection from predators. Bird baths can be set up but should be

placed so that the wet birds can easily get to sheltering shrubbery if they are attacked. A variety of bird houses can be constructed and appropriately placed. These will attract a variety of birds and it is fun to watch the parents building their nests and caring for their young.

If you feed birds during the winter, be sure to continue putting food out every day because the birds learn to depend upon it and if they should suddenly be deprived they may starve before they can find another source.

EXAMPLES OF BIRD HOUSES
AND FEEDING STATIONS

INDEX